NICK CAVE ANTHO

WISE PUBLICATIONS
LONDON / NEW YORK / SYDNEY / PARIS / COPENHAGEN / MADRID / TOKYO

PUBLISHED BY
WISE PUBLICATIONS
14-15 BERNERS STREET, LONDON W1T 3LJ, UK.

EXCLUSIVE DISTRIBUTORS:

MUSIC SALES LIMITED
DISTRIBUTION CENTRE, NEWMARKET ROAD,
BURY ST EDMUNDS, SUFFOLK, IP33 3YB, UK.

MUSIC SALES PTY LIMITED
20 RESOLUTION DRIVE, CARINGBAH,
NSW 2229, AUSTRALIA.

ORDER NO. AM969133
ISBN 0-7119-8681-9
THIS BOOK © COPYRIGHT 2001 BY WISE PUBLICATIONS,
A DIVISION OF MUSIC SALES LIMITED.

COVER DESIGN BY PHIL GAMBRILL.
MUSIC ARRANGED BY DEREK JONES.
MUSIC ENGRAVED BY PAUL EWERS MUSIC DESIGN.
COVER IMAGES: POLLY BORLAND/KATZ PICTURES.
INSIDE IMAGE: JOE DILWORTH.

PRINTED IN THE EU.

YOUR GUARANTEE OF QUALITY:
AS PUBLISHERS, WE STRIVE TO PRODUCE EVERY
BOOK TO THE HIGHEST COMMERCIAL STANDARDS.
THE MUSIC HAS BEEN FRESHLY ENGRAVED AND
THE BOOK HAS BEEN CAREFULLY DESIGNED TO MINIMISE
AWKWARD PAGE TURNS AND TO MAKE PLAYING
FROM IT A REAL PLEASURE.
PARTICULAR CARE HAS BEEN GIVEN TO SPECIFYING
ACID-FREE, NEUTRAL-SIZED
PAPER MADE FROM PULPS WHICH HAVE NOT BEEN
ELEMENTAL CHLORINE BLEACHED.
THIS PULP IS FROM FARMED SUSTAINABLE FORESTS
AND WAS PRODUCED WITH SPECIAL REGARD
FOR THE ENVIRONMENT.
THROUGHOUT, THE PRINTING AND BINDING
HAVE BEEN PLANNED TO ENSURE A STURDY,
ATTRACTIVE PUBLICATION WHICH SHOULD
GIVE YEARS OF ENJOYMENT.
IF YOUR COPY FAILS TO MEET OUR HIGH
STANDARDS, PLEASE INFORM US AND WE WILL
GLADLY REPLACE IT.

WWW.MUSICSALES.COM

(ARE YOU) THE ONE THAT I'VE BEEN WAITING FOR?

Words & Music by Nick Cave

♩ = 68

Capo 3rd Fret

Cm

Cm
1. I felt you com-ing girl,
(Verses 2 & 3 see block lyrics)

Eb
as you drew near,___

Ab9
I knew you'd find___ me cos I

Eb
longed you here.___

Are you my des - ti - ny? Is this how you'll ap - pear,_____ wrapped in a coat_

_____ with the tears in your eyes?_____ Well take that coat babe and

throw it on_____ the floor,_____ are you the one that

I've been wait-ing for?_____

To Coda ⊕ 1.

⊕ Coda

Stars   have their mo- ment,   then they___ die.___

Are   you   the   one   that   I've been   wait - ing   for?

Verse 2:

As you've been moving surely toward me
My soul has comforted and assured me
That in time my heart it will reward me
And that all will be revealed
So I've sat and watched the ice age thaw
Are you the one that I've been looking for?

Verse 3:

There's a man who spoke wonders though I've never met him
He said "He who seeks finds, and who knocks will be let in"
I think of you in motion and just how close you are getting
And how every little thing anticipates you
All down my veins my heart strings call
Are you the one I've been waiting for?

AND NO MORE SHALL WE PART

Words & Music by Nick Cave

Verse 2:
And no more shall we part
All the hatchets have been buried now
And all of the birds will sing to your beautiful heart
Upon the bough
And no more shall we part
Your chain of command had been silenced now
And all of those birds would have sung to your beautiful heart
Anyhow.

AS I SAT SADLY BY HER SIDE

Words & Music by Nick Cave

-en___ wide.___ We pressed our fa-ces to the glass as

I sat sad-ly by her___ side.___

2. She said,

3. Then she___ smiled___ and turned to me___ and___ wait-ed for me___
(Verses 5 & 7 see block lyrics)

gent - ly pass___ ov - er to me___ and a - gain we pressed our diff-'rent fa - ces___ to the glass.___ "That may be ve - ry well," I said___ "but watch the one fall - ing in the street.___ See him ges - ture to his neigh - bours and see him tram-pled be -

Verse 2:

She said "Father, mother, sister, brother
Uncle, aunt, nephew, niece
Soldier, sailor, physician, labourer
Actor, scientist, mechanic, priest
Earth and moon and sun and stars
And planets and comets with tails blazing
All are there forever falling
Falling lovely and amazing"

Verse 5:

With trembling hand I turned toward her
And pushed the hair out of her eyes
The kitten jumped back to her lap
As I sat sadly by her side.

Verse 6:

Then she drew the curtains down
And said, "When will you ever learn
That what happens there beyond the glass
Is simply none of your concern?
God has given you but one heart
You are not a home for the hearts of your brothers
And God don't care for your benevolence
Anymore than he cares for the lack of it in others
Nor does he care for you to sit
At windows in judgement of the world he created
While sorrows pile up around you
Ugly, useless and over-inflated."

Verse 7:

At which she turned her head away
Great tears leaping from her eyes
I could not wipe the smile from my face
As I sat sadly by her side.

THE CARNY

Words & Music by Nick Cave

Spoken: Verses 5&6 see block lyrics

Spoken: Verse 7 see block lyric

Spoken: Verse 9 see block lyric

Spoken: Verse 10 see block lyric

Cdim

Cm

And the rain it ham-mered down, the rain___ it ham-mered down, and the rain

___ it ham-mered down. And the rain it ham - mered down.

28

Verse 2:
Dog boy, Atlas, Mandrake, the geeks, the hired hands
There was not one among them that did not cast an eye behind
In the hope that the carney would return to his own kind.

Verse 3:
The carney left behind a horse
All skin and bone that he named Sorrow
And it was a shallow, unmarked grave
That the old nag was laid in the then parched meadow.

Verse 4:
And it was dwarves were given the task of digging the ditch
And laying the nag's carcass in the ground
While boss Bollini, waving his smoking pistol around saying
"The nag was dead meat, we can't afford to carry dead weight"
While the whole company standing about not making a sound
And turning to the dwarves perched on the enclosure gate
The boss says "Bury this lump of crow bait."

Verse 5:
And then the rain came hammering down
Everybody running for their wagons
Tying all the canvas flaps down
The mangy cats growling in their cages
The bird-girl flapping and squawking around.

Verse 6:
The whole valley reeking of wet beast
Wet beast and rotten sun hay
Freak and brute creation packed up and on their way
The three dwarves peering from their wagons hind
Moses says to Noah "We should'da dug a deeper one"
Their grizzled faces like dying moons still dirty from the digging done.

Verse 7:
And Charley the oldest of the three said
"I guess the carney ain't gonna show"
Then they were silent for a spell
Wishing they had done a better job of burying Sorrow.

Verse 8:
And as the company passed from the valley into higher ground
And the rain beat on the ridge and on the meadow, and on the mound
Until nothing was left, nothing left at all, except the body of Sorrow
That rose in time to float upon the surface of the eaten soil.

Verse 9:
And a murder of crows did circle around
First one, then the others flapping blackly down.

Verse 10:
And the carney's van still sat upon the edge
Tilting slowly as the firm ground turned to sludge.

DEANNA

Words & Music by Nick Cave

Oh De-an - na, oh, oh, De - an - na.__
(Chorus 3 see block lyric)

Ah De - an - na.__ Well you know you are my

friend now and I ain't down here for your mo-

To Coda

- ney, and I ain't down here for your love,___ I ain't___ down here for your mo - ney, I'm down here for your soul.

There's no car - pet on the floor_____ and the wind - ing clock holds ma - ny moths. A - round your Klu - klux fur - ni - ture,

into their heads_____ on this mean_____ sea-

-son   but this lit-tle An-gel that I'm squeez-ing,   she ain't been mean to

Oh   De - an - na,   oh, oh,   De - an - na.

I   a-am a knock-ing   with my tool box and my stock-ing,

and don't wor-ry 'bout what it hits cos it ain't yours to

sin. Oh De - an - na, cos it just ain't yours to sin.
(Chorus 5 see block lyric)

Ah sw - eet De - an - na,___ I ain't get - ting a - ny

young - er. And you're my friend. Well I ain't

Chorus 3:
(Oh Deanna)
Oh Deanna
Well you are my friend and my partner
On this house on the hill
And I ain't down here for your money
No I ain't down here for your love
I ain't down here for your love or money
I'm down here for your soul.

Chorus 5:
The sun a hump on my shoulder
And I don't intend getting older
Oh Deanna.

DO YOU LOVE ME?

Words & Music by Nick Cave

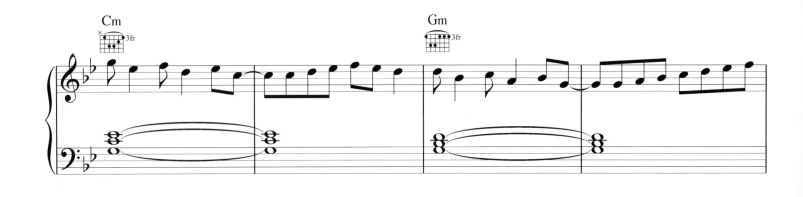

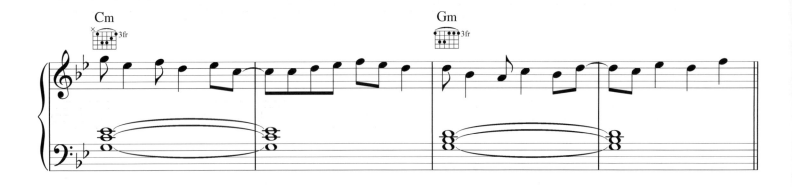

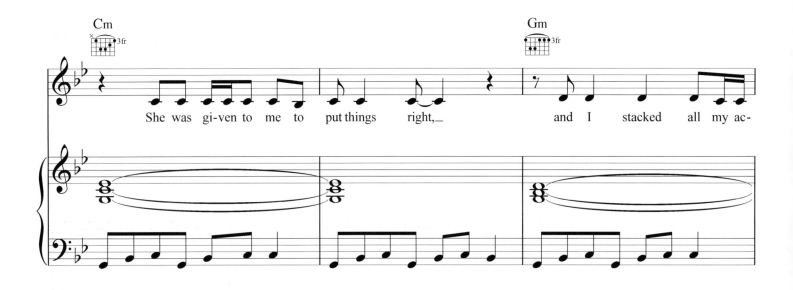

She was gi-ven to me to put things right,__ and I stacked all my ac-

-comp-lish-ments be - side her. Yet I seemed so ob - se - lete and small,

FROM HER TO ETERNITY

Words & Music by Nick Cave

For spoken text 1 see block lyric

I start to

cry.___

I start to cry.

Oh I hear her

walk - ing,___ walk-ing bare-foot cross the floor - boards.

All through this lone - some___ night.

I hear her cry - ing too.___ Hot tears come splash-ing down,

leak-ing through the cracks,___ down up-on my___ face. Catch'em in my___

___ mouth. Catch'em in my___ mouth. Catch'em in my___ mouth. Ah catch'em

in my mouth. Ah walk and cry.___ Walk and cry.___ Ah,

walk and cry.___ Ah, walk and cry. From

her_____ ah, to_____ e-

-ter - ni-ty._____ From her_____ to_____ e-

-ter - ni-ty._____ From her_____ to e-

Play 4 times

-ter - ni-ty._____ *For spoken text 2 see block lyric*

52

why   don't tell me lie.   Why the   ceil-ing still shakes,   shake, shake,

Play 9 times

shake.   And all__ the   fix-tures turn to ser-pents   and snakes.

For spoken text 4 see block lyric

Go!   From

her_____   ah to_____

56

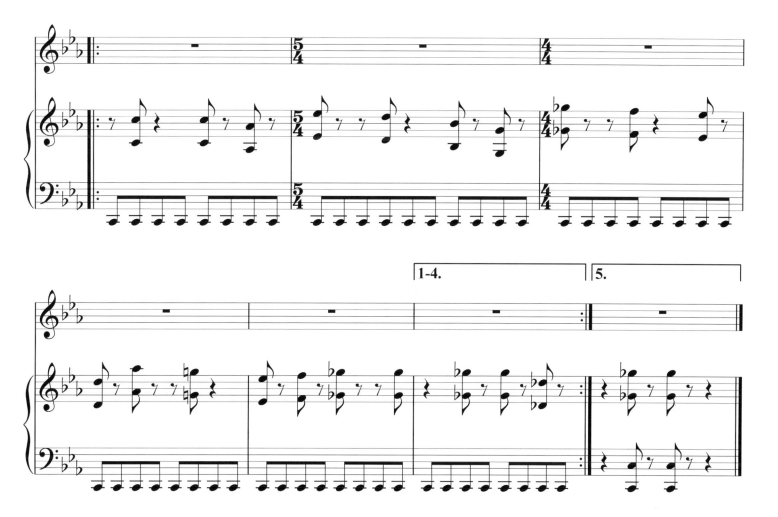

Spoken text 1:
I wanna tell you about a girl
You know, she lives in room 29
Why that's the one right up top a mine.

Spoken text 2:
I read her diary on the sheets
Scrutinizing every little bit of dirt
Tore out a page and stuff it inside my shirt
I fled outta the window
And shinning it down the vine
Outta her nightmare and into mine.

Spoken text 3:
She's wearing those blue stockings I bet
And standing like this with my ear to the ceiling
Listen I know it must sound absurd
But I can hear the most melancholy sound I ever heard
Walk and cry, walk and cry.

Spoken text 4:
This desire to possess her is a wound
And it's nagging me like a shrew
But I know that to possess her
Is therefore not to desire her
Oh, oh,oh, then ya know, that little girl
Would just have to go.

INTO MY ARMS

Words & Music by Nick Cave

I don't be-lieve___ in an in-ter-ven-tion-ist___ God.___

But I know darl - ing that you do.___

But if I did___ I would kneel down and ask him,

not to in - ter - vene___ when it came to you.___

Well not to touch a hair___ on your head, leave you as___ you are,___ if he felt he had___ to di-

Verse 3:
But I believe in love
And I know that you do too
And I believe in some kind of path
That we can walk down me and you
So keep your candles burning
Make a journey bright and pure
That you'll keep returning
Always and evermore.

Into my arms *etc.*

HENRY LEE

Words: Traditional
Music by Nick Cave

1. Get down, get down, lit-tle Hen-ry Lee and
(Verses 2-5 see block lyric)

stay all night with me._____ You won't, find a girl_____ in

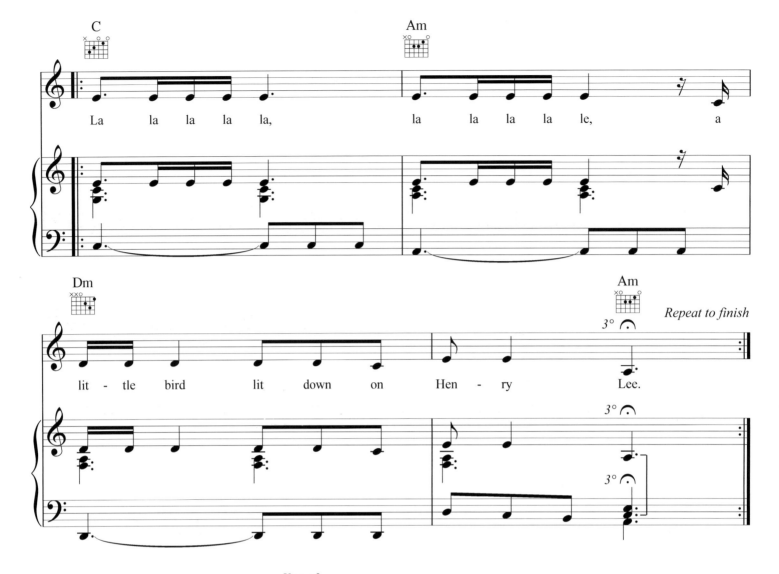

Verse 2:
I can't get down and I won't get down
And stay all night with thee
For the girl I have in that merry green land
I love far better than thee
And the wind did howl and the wind did blow…

Verse 3:
She leaned herself against a fence
Just for a kiss or two
And with a little pen-knife held in her hand
She plugged him through and through
And the wind did roar and the wind did moan…

Verse 4:
Come take him by his lily-white hands
Come take him by his feet
And throw him down this deep deep well
Which is more than one hundred feet
And the wind did howl and the wind did blow…

Verse 5:
Lie there, lie there, little Henry Lee
Till the flesh drops from your bones
For the girl you have in that merry green land
Can wait forever for you to come home
And the wind did howl and the wind did moan…

THE MERCY SEAT

Words By Nick Cave
Music by Nick Cave & Mick Harvey

And the mer - cy seat is burn - ing and I think my head is glow - ing,
(Verse 6 see block lyric)

and in a way I'm hop - ing to be done with all this weigh - ing up___ of

truth. An eye for an eye, and a tooth for a tooth. And I've got no - thing left to loose___ and I'm not a - fraid to

7. And the mer - cy seat is wait - ing, And I think my head is burn - ing

and in a way I'm yearn-ing to be done with all the mea-sur-ing___ of

proof. A life for a life and a truth for a truth and a-ny-way___ there was no

proof and I'm not a - fraid to die. And the mer - cy seat is wait - ing

and I think my head is smok - ing. And in a way I'm hop - ing to be

Verse 1:

I began to warm and chill to objects and their fields
A ragged cup, a twisted mop, the face of Jesus in my soup
Those sinister dinner deals, the meal trolley's wicked wheels
A hooked bone rising from my food
All things either good or ungood.

Verse 2:

Interpret signs and catalogue, a blackened tooth, a scarlet frog
The walls are bad, black bottom kind they are the sick breath at my hind
They are the sick breath at my hind, they are the sick breath at my hind
They are the sick breath gathering at my hind.

Verse 3:

Like my good hand I tattooed EVIL across it's brothers fist
That filthy five! They did nothing to challenge or resist.

Verse 4:

My kill hand is called evil, wears a wedding band that's good
'Tis a long suffering shackle collaring all that rebel blood.

Chorus 6:

And the mercy seat is waiting, and I think my head is burning
And in a way I'm yearning to be done with all this measuring of proof
An eye for an eye and a tooth for a tooth
And anyway there was no proof and nor a motive why.

Chorus 9:

And the mercy seat is waiting, and I think my head is burning
And in a way I'm yearning to be done with all this measuring of proof
And eye for an eye and a tooth for a tooth
And anyway I told the truth but I'm not afraid to lie.

Chorus 10:

And the mercy seat is waiting, and I think my head is burning
And in a way I'm yearning to be done with all this measuring of proof
And eye for an eye and a tooth for a tooth
And anyway I told the truth and I'm afraid I told a lie.

NOBODY'S BABY NOW

Words & Music by Nick Cave

1. I've searched the ho-ly books,
(Verse 2 see block lyric)

I've tried to un-ra-vel

the mys - tery of Je - sus Christ, the Sa - viour.

I read the po - ets and the

an - a - lysts, searched through the books on hu - man be -

- ha - viour.

I've tra-velled this world___ a - round___ for an ans - wer that re - fused to be found.__ I don't know why and I don't know how,___ but she's no - bo - dy's ba - by now.___

3. This is her dress___ that I loved the best, with the blue___ quilt-ed vio-lets a-cross the breast.___ And these are my ma-ny let-ters torn to pie-ces by long fin-

Verse 2:

I loved her then and I guess I love her still

Hers is the face I see when a certain mood moves in

She lives in my blood and skin

Her wild feral stare, her dark hair

Her winter lips as cold as stone

Yeah I was her man

But there are some things love won't allow

I held her hand but I don't hold it now

I don't know why and I don't know how

But she's nobody's baby now.

THE SHIP SONG

Words & Music by Nick Cave

Chorus 1: Come sail your ships a-round me
(Chorus 2 see block lyric)
and burn your
bri - ges down.___ We make a lit - tle his - tory ba - by

Chorus 2:
Come loose your doubts upon me
And let your hair hang down
You are a little mystery to me
Every time you call around

Verse 2:
Your face has fallen sad now
'Fore you know the time is nigh
When I must remove your ways
And you, you must try to fly.

Come sail your ships *etc.*

STRAIGHT TO YOU

Words & Music by Nick Cave

Now_ hea-ven has de-nied_ us its king-dom and the saints they're all drunk_ and howl-ing at the moon._ And the cha-ri-ots_ of an - gels are col-lid- -ing. Well I'll run ba - by but I'll_ come run-ning, straight to

Verse 2:
Now the light in our window is fading
And the candleit gutters on the ledge
Well now sorrow, it comes a-stealing
And I'll cry girl, but I'll come a-running.

Straight to you *etc.*

STRANGER THAN KINDNESS

Words by Anita Lane
Music by Blixa Bargeld

1. Strang - er___ than kind - ness.___
(Verse 2 see block lyric)

Bot - tled light from ho - tels.___

98

Verse 2:
You caress yourself
And grind my soft cold bones below
Your map of my desire
Burned in your flesh
Even a fool can come
A strange lit stair
And find a rope hanging there
Stranger than kindness.

RED RIGHT HAND

Words by Nick Cave
Music by Nick Cave, Mick Harvey & Thomas Wydler

1. Take a lit-tle walk to the
(Verses 2 & 3 see block lyric)

edge of town_ and go a-cross the track, where the

vi-a-duct looms like a bird of doom_ as it shifts and cracks.

You'll see him in your night-mares, you'll see him in your dreams.

He'll ap - pear out of no - where but he

ain't — what he seems.___ You'll see him in your head,___

___ on the T. V. screen.___ Hey bud-dy I'm warn-ing you to turn it off.

He's a ghost, he's a god, he's a man, he's a gu - ru.___

You're one mi-cro-scop-ic cog in his cat-a-stro-phic plan, de-

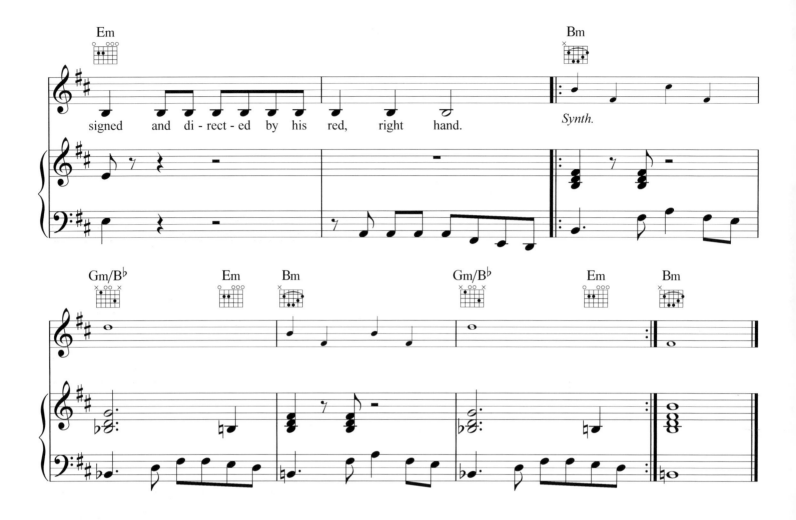

signed and di-rect-ed by his red, right hand.

Synth.

Em   Bm

Gm/B♭   Em   Bm   Gm/B♭   Em   Bm

Verse 2:

He'll wrap you in his arms
Tell you that you've been a good boy
He'll rekindle all the dreams
It took you a lifetime to destroy
He'll reach deep into the hole
Heal your shrinking soul
But there won't be a single thing that you can do
He's a god, he's a man
He's a ghost, he's a guru
They're whispering his name
Through this disappearing land
But hidden in his coat
Is a red right hand.

Verse 3:

You don't have no money?
He'll get you some
You don't have no car?
He'll get you one
You don't have no self respect
You feel like an insect
Well don't you worry buddy
'Cause here he comes
Throught the ghetto and the barrio
And the bowery and the slum
A shadow is cast wherever he stands.

Stacks of green paper in his red right hand *etc.*

TUPELO

Words by Nick Cave
Music by Barry Adamson & Mick Harvey

come to Tu-pe-lo.___ Come to Tu-pe-lo.___

Yon-der on__ the ho-ri - zon. Yon-der on__ the ho-ri - zon. Stopped at the might - y riv-er___

sucked the damn__ thing dry. Dis-tant thun - der rum - bles,__ dis-tant thun - der rum - bles.__

Rum-ble hum - bly like the beast,__ the beast it com-eth, com-eth down. Beast it com-eth, com-eth down, the

nag is spooked and cra-zi-er.___ God help Tu-pe-lo.___ Oh, God help Tu-pe-lo.___ You can

say these streets are riv-ers,_____ you can call these riv-ers streets. You can

tell your-self you're dream-ing bud-dy, but no___ sleep runs this deep, no,

no sleep runs this deep. Oh, God help Tu-pe-lo.___ Oh,

110

God help Tu-pe-lo.___ Oh, God help Tu-pe-lo.___ Oh, God help Tu-pe-lo.___

Oh, go to sleep lit-tle child-ren.___ The

Sand-man's on his way. Oh go to sleep lit-tle child-ren, the

Sand-man's on his way. Lis-ten to the beat-ing of___ their blood, lis-ten to the beat-ing of their blood.

God help_ in Tu-pe-lo.__ God help_ the Tu-pe-lo__ The rain come down,_

the rain come down. The King will walk on Tu-pe-lo, the King will walk on Tu-pe-lo, the

King will walk on Tu-pe-lo.__ He'll car-ry the bur-den of Tu-pe-lo.__ He'll car-ry the bur-den yeah, of

Tu-pe-lo,_____ he'll car-ry the bur-den of Tu-pe-lo. Tu-pe-

WHERE THE WILD ROSES GROW

Words & Music by Nick Cave

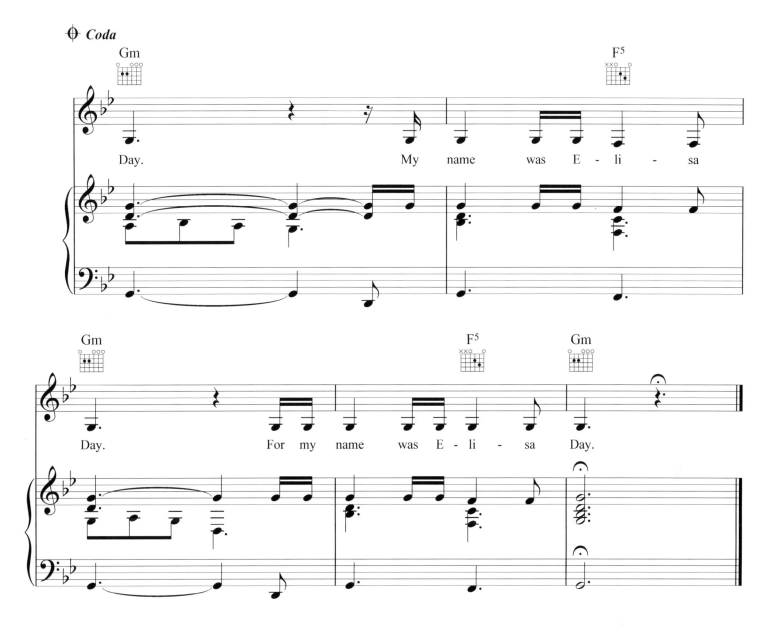

Coda

Day.   My name was E - li - sa

Day.   For my name was E - li - sa Day.

Verse 2:

(MAN)   On the second day I brought her a flower
She was more beautiful than any woman I'd seen
I said, "Do you know where the wild roses grow
So sweet and scarlet and free?"

(GIRL)   On the second he came with a single red rose
He said "Give me your loss and your sorrow"
I nodded my head, as I lay on the bed
"If I show you the roses will you follow?"

Verse 3:

(GIRL)   On the third day he took me to the river
He showed me the roses and we kissed
And the last thing I heard was a muttered word
As he knelt above me with a rock in his fist.

(MAN)   On the last day I took her where the wild roses grow
And she lay on the bank, the wind light as a thief
And I kissed her goodbye, said, "All beauty must die"
And I leant down and planted a rose 'tween her teeth.

THE WEEPING SONG

Words & Music by Nick Cave

2. Fa - ther, why are all the wo-men weep- ing?
(Verse 3 see block lyric)

They are all weep-ing for their men.

Then why___ are all the men there weep- ing?

They are weep - ing back___

Verse 3:
Father, why are all the children weeping?
They are merely crying son
Oh, are they merely crying, father?
Yes, true weeping is yet to come.

This is a weeping song *etc.*